Beach Babe

Barbara Mitchelhill

Published in association with
The Basic Skills Agency

Hodder & Stoughton
A MEMBER OF THE HODDER

Acknowledgements
Cover: Darren Lock
Illustrations: Jim Eldridge

Orders: please contact Bookpoint Ltd, 39 Milton Park, Abingdon, Oxon OX14
4TD. Telephone: (44) 01235 400414, Fax: (44) 01235 400454. Lines are open
from 9.00–6.00, Monday to Saturday, with a 24 hour message answering
service. Email address: orders@bookpoint.co.uk

British Library Cataloguing in Publication Data
A catalogue record for this title is available from The British Library

ISBN 0 340 74321 2

First published 1999
Impression number   10 9 8 7 6 5 4 3 2
Year   2004 2003 2002 2001 2000 1999

Copyright © 1999 Barbara Mitchelhill

Typeset by by Fakenham Photosetting Ltd, Fakenham, Norfolk.
Printed in Great Britain for Hodder & Stoughton Educational, a division of
Hodder Headline Plc, 338 Euston Road, London NW1 3BH by Athenaeum
Press Ltd, Gateshead, Tyne & Wear.

About the play

The People
- Alpa
- Lou

The Time

Around lunch time.

The Scene

A beach in summer.

Act 1

Alpa   You've been in a mood
all morning, Megan.
We didn't ask you to come with us.
You just wanted
to show off your new bikini.

(*pause*)

Lou   Go on. Admit it, Megan!
Just because your dad
gave you twenty quid.
You're spoilt, you are!

Alpa   Don't speak to her, Lou.
She's having one of her sulks.
Let's dig a hole in the sand
and put her in it.

They laugh.

Lou   Aaahhh! Have we scared you off?
(shouting)
Go on!
Have a swim on your own.
We're not coming with you!
Hey, Alpa,
she's got a real big bum, hasn't she?

Alpa   *(shouting)*
Yeah! Good riddance.
I hope the sharks get you!

Lou   *(laughing)*
I bet she won't go in the sea.
Just watch!

Alpa   You're right.
She's paddling like a kid.

Lou	Well, I'm going to sunbathe.
	It's nice just the two of us.
	We don't want her showing off.
Alpa	Lou!
Lou	Yeah?
Alpa	Those boys playing beach ball
	– they're looking at Megan.
Lou	So what's new?
	Before long, they'll be after her.
Alpa	Yeah. What's new?
	She's a right flirt
	and she's wearing next to nothing.
Lou	Boys always go after her.
	Even when she's fully dressed
	they drool over her.
Alpa	They're supposed to be
	playing beach ball.
Lou	Huh! Look at 'em!
	They're drooling over Megs
	in her red bikini.
	She's a real beach babe.
	She's pretending not to see them.

Alpa	I wish she'd go in for a swim.
	Then they'll get on with their game.
Lou	No way!
	Megs *wants* them to drool over her.
	She likes being
	the centre of attention.
	She's enjoying every minute.
	She won't go in the water.
Alpa	I bet she'll make a big splash.
	Pretend to drown.
	Then they'll all come rushing over
	to save her.
Lou	She'd like that.
Alpa	Yeah. The drama queen.
Lou	Well, something will happen.
	It's just a matter of time.
	Huh! What a show off.
Alpa	Doesn't she know
	how obvious she is?
Lou	Just like one of those blonde bimbos
	on *Baywatch*.

Alpa   I bet those boys will ask her
to join in the game.
Any minute now,
they'll throw the ball over.

(*pause*)

Lou   Yep. You're right. There it goes.
Alpa   Oooops! The ball's hit her.
(*laughing*)
Good shot!
Serves her right!
Lou   I bet that gorgeous guy
with dark hair goes over to her.
Watch.
I give him five seconds.
1 ... 2 ... 3 ... 4 ...
Alpa   Yep! There he goes.
Wow! What a hunk!
I'd give anything to bump into him.
He's got muscles
like you've never seen before!

Lou	Oh no!
	Megs is pretending to be hurt.
	I don't believe it.
	She's just acting.
	That beach ball wouldn't hurt a fly.
Alpa	He won't fall for a trick like that, will he?
Lou	Only if he wants to.
Alpa	Huh! I think he wants to!
	He's bending over her
	as if she was a little princess.
	I'm going to throw up.
	This is gross.
Lou	He's rubbing her arm. Cor!
	He could rub my arm any time.
Alpa	Maybe he wouldn't want
	to rub *your* arm.
Lou	Says who?

Alpa   Says me.
You're not exactly
a blonde bimbo, are you?
And you haven't got a rich daddy,
have you?
And you don't have gorgeous hunks
running after you.

Lou   No. I just sit here
on this beach towel.
On this stupid holiday.
Talking to my stupid friend.

Alpa   Not that stupid!
I brought a picnic, didn't I?

Lou   Oh you're brilliant really, Alpa!
I'm starving.
What you got?

Alpa   Crisps, sandwiches, chocolate
and something to drink.

Lou   Cool! Let's eat it
before Megs gets back.
Let her starve, eh?

Alpa	Yeah.
	Just look at her –
	jumping about and
	pretending to catch the ball.
	She's just showing off.
Lou	You'd think she'd ask us over.
	That's what friends are for, after all.
	(*sighing*)
	I bet they're having
	a great time.
Alpa	Have a sandwich.
Lou	Ta.
	(*sighs again*)
	A sandwich doesn't taste so good
	when you'd rather be playing
	beach ball.
Alpa	No.
Lou	Will you pass the crisps?
Alpa	Salt and vinegar or smoky bacon?
Lou	I don't care. I'm too fed up.

They start eating the crisps.

Alpa   Ooh look! They're stopping.
That blond one's
looking at his watch.

Lou   Maybe they're going
for something to eat.

Alpa   Invite 'em over, Lou.
Give 'em a shout.

Lou   I daren't.

Alpa   'Course you dare. Go on.

Lou   OK – but pass my bag.

Alpa   What for?

Lou   I want to comb my hair first.

*Alpa passes the bag and
Lou looks inside it.*

I should have a lipstick in here, too.

Alpa   Lou, you're just going
to ask them over.
You're not going on a date.
Get on with it.

Lou runs a comb through her hair and gets to her feet.

Lou   Do I look all right?
           I don't look fat in this, do I?
Alpa   You look OK. Go on.
Lou   (*shouting*)
           HEY YOU GUYS!
           WANT SOMETHING TO EAT?

           (*pause*)

           MEGAN'S OUR FRIEND.
           COME AND JOIN US.

           (*pause*)

Alpa   I don't think they heard you, Lou
           Let's try together.
Lou   Yeah. We'll say 'Come and join us'.
           OK? 1 ... 2 ... 3 ...

Alpa & Lou   COME AND JOIN US.

(*pause*)

Alpa   It's no good.
They're walking away
towards the prom.
I bet they're going to a cafe.

Lou   They're taking Megs with them.
Just our luck.

Alpa   Yeah. Just our luck
that they've got
a gorgeous sports car.

Lou   Wherc?

Alpa   Up on the prom.

Lou   You mean that gorgeous silver one?

Alpa   Yes.

Lou   It must have cost a fortune.
It can't be theirs.

Alpa   I bet it is.

Lou	Right. I bet you
	that piece of chocolate
	it's not their car.
Alpa	Right. I bet it is.
Lou	They're getting nearer.
Alpa	They're going towards it.
Lou	They're going to pass it. ... Yes!
	No!
Alpa	I win.
	The one in the green shorts
	has the key.
	It must be his car.
	Pass the chocolate.
Lou	Hey, she's not getting in.
	And neither is the guy
	in the blue shorts.
Alpa	Why are they opening the boot?
Lou	Don't ask me.
Alpa	They're taking something out.
	What is it? Can you see?

17

Lou	It's a lilo, I think.
	One of those things you blow up.
	You know.
	I think Megs and Blue Shorts
	are taking it back to the beach.
Alpa	Huh! So they're staying behind.
	Typical!
	She's a real fast worker, she is.
	Just watch it.
	She'll have a date tonight.
	We'll be by ourselves
	and she'll be with Blue Shorts.
Lou	Yeah. I'm fed up.
	Pass the crisps.
Alpa	We've eaten them all.
	There's only drink left and that's flat.
Lou	Doom! What a holiday.
Alpa	They're blowing up the lilo now.
Lou	I couldn't care less, Alpa.
	I'm going to sunbathe.
	At least I'll go home with a tan.
	Where's the sun tan lotion?
Alpa	In the bag. Here you are.

She passes the sun tan lotion.

Lou   Rub some on my back, will you?
            I don't want to burn.
Alpa   Right then. Roll over.

Alpa *starts to rub sun tan lotion
onto* **Lou***'s back.*

            You could get a tan
            but that cloud's
            going to block out the sun!
Lou   Mmmm.
Alpa   Don't go to sleep on me, Lou.
            I don't want to sit here
            with nobody to talk to,
            watching those two having fun.
Lou   Mmmm.
Alpa   They're blowing up the lilo, Lou.
Lou   Mmmm.

Alpa	They're running towards the water.
Lou	Mmmm.
Alpa	You're not listening are you?
	Stay awake, Lou.
	Don't drift off.

(*pause*)

Megs and Blue Shorts
are riding on the lilo.
Floating over the waves.
It looks great.
Pity the sun's going in.
The sky's all cloudy.

Lou	(*sitting up*)
	Yeah! Brrr! I'm cold.
	Pass my T-shirt, will you?
	There's no way I'll get a tan now.
Alpa	Lou!
Lou	Yeah? (*pulling on her T-shirt*)

Alpa   Megs and Blue Shorts
are a long way from the beach.
Look!

*They stand up and
look at the horizon.*

Lou   Cor! You're right.

Alpa   They should never
have gone on that lilo.
It's dangerous.
Lilos blow away ever so quickly.

Lou   So?
Maybe she'll drift across to America.
Maybe we'll never see her again
– if we're lucky!

Alpa   Don't say that!
She's our friend really.
I wish she hadn't
gone out on that thing.

Lou	There's a dangerous current
	on that side of the bay.
	That's what's taking them out to sea.
Alpa	Do you think they know about it?
Lou	I don't suppose Megs does.
	She's just a beach babe.
	She thinks a current
	is something you find in a bun!
Alpa	Don't joke, Lou!
	I'm getting worried.
	Come on! Let's run down the beach.
	See if we can warn them
	about the current.
Lou	Right! I'm with you Alpa.

They run down to the water's edge

Alpa	Let's shout together.
	1 ... 2 ... 3 ...
Alpa & Lou	LOOK OUT, MEGS!
	THERE'S A CURRENT.
	COME BACK.

Lou   Do you think she heard us?

Alpa   No. Let's try again.

Alpa & Lou   COME BACK, MEGS!

Lou   I think she heard!

Alpa   Yes! Look!

          They're waving.

Lou   Are you sure?

          I think they're calling for help.

Alpa   You're right!

          Come on, Lou.

          We've got to do something.

          There's a call box up on the prom.

          We'll ring the police.

          They'll know what to do.

          They run to a call box and
          dial the police.

Lou   Hello. Can you help, please?
My friend's in trouble.

(*pause*)

I'm ringing from the call box
at Benning Bay.

(*pause*)

It's my friend, Megan.
She's out on a lilo
with her boyfriend.
They've been taken by the current.
They're drifting out to sea
and they can't get back.

(*pause*)

Yes, we'll wait on the beach.
Thank you. Bye.

Alpa   What did they say?

Lou They'll send a lifeboat
and a police car right away.

Alpa I'm really scared.
It'll take ages before they come.
It might be too late.

Lou We did what we could, Alpa.
The police said
we'd done the right thing.

Alpa	I can't see it.
Lou	Why?
Alpa	Because it was all our fault.
	We said all those nasty things
	to Megan.
	That's why she went off
	in the first place.
Lou	You're right.

(*pause*)

	I've always wanted a bikini like that.
Alpa	And I always wanted to be skinny
	like Megs.
Lou	Let's make a pact.
	If Megan gets out of this alive,
	we'll be the best friends
	she ever had.
Alpa	Agreed.

The sound of a police siren.